Mary Rose

Beginning Public Speaking

Student Workpack

Interactive Video Curriculum
2 DVDs . . . 10 Lessons

A super simple,
user friendly,
no experience needed,
easy to follow
program for introducing
and
building public speaking skills
for the Christian student
(and teacher).

Teresa M. Moon

Let your conversation be always full of grace,
seasoned with salt that you may know how to answer everyone.
. . . Colossians 4:6

Published by
Communicators Advantage Project (CAP)

Developed for
Institute for Cultural Communicators (ICC)
www.instituteforculturalcommunicators.org

Beginning Public Speaking
Student Workpack

To be used in conjunction with Beginning Public Speaking Teacher's Edition and Beginning Public Speaking DVD.

First Edition, 2002
Second Edition, 2006
Third Edition, 2010

Cover design: Jessie McLean

ISBN: 978 -0-9724612-3-8

To the many students who have motivated me to better teach communication skills by their desire to master them.

To all the Interns who have assisted me in developing these tools to equip communicators for Christ.

It has been a humbling privilege to be your mentor and to learn from you along the way. I am very proud of you.

Teresa Moon

Ars Rhetoricae: The Art of Public Speaking

Nothing that man can do is more powerful than communication. In an age of atomic power, super computers, and the double helix, the spoken word still stands alone in its ability to move men's hearts. Thus, I can think of nothing I have learned in my academic career which is more valuable than the arts of rhetoric, communication, and public speaking. Regardless of how much scientific power the world harnesses, the course of history will always be shaped by those who can effectively get their ideas across, whether their names are Adolf Hitler, John F. Kennedy, or Martin Luther King, Jr. Given the dynamic power of public communication, Christians are the ones who should be the most excited about harnessing and using it, as we are the ones with the truth.

In the years since I began my involvement in speech classes and competitions, I have been greatly blessed by these skills in almost every area of my life. When standing for my beliefs among friends, in the classroom, or while witnessing, the ability to shape and articulate ideas and arguments has been fundamentally necessary to get the Christian message across. In everyday life, when somebody asks you, "Oh, really? Why do you believe that?" you are not given two hours with a pastor and a catechism to formulate your answer. You have to be ready and willing to backup what you are saying right there, on the spot. Basic communications skills make the difference between a potent witnessing opportunity and a pointless disagreement. Because of this, I believe very strongly that the lessons of rhetoric and public speaking can have an impact on the world -- an opportunity which we, as Christians, must not ignore.

Thane Rehn

Thane, age seventeen at the time he wrote this article, has used his public speaking skills to earn national and world titles in high school and college competition as well as to influence students and professors about issues that were important to him. At the time of this printing, he is applying his communication skills as an attorney.

Public Speaking Class Meeting Schedule

Encouragement for Parents & Teachers

My two daughters have taken public speaking, using the lessons included in this curriculum, from Teresa Moon for five years in a row, and, with very few exceptions, I have attended every class with them. It has been delightful to watch not only my daughters' progress, but also the progress of other children. I have seen terrified, teary-eyed children and teens turned into confident speakers who look forward to their turn to speak.

Teresa has always taught the students to give positive comments to each other, as well as constructive suggestions after each speech. Learning these great skills in a totally positive environment, builds the kids' confidence immeasurably.

I'm thrilled that my children have been able to sit under Teresa's teaching. Whenever they are asked to speak in public they do it without a moment's hesitation. I know that these skills will help to equip them to serve God without fear.

I, too, have learned great public speaking skills during the last five years. I have used my skills to give announcements in church, to perform in plays and skits, and to sing on a worship team. I love serving God in this way, and I love seeing my children willing to participate at even earlier ages.

Twyla Stewart

Twyla is the mother of Public Speaking students ... who eventually learned she could teach public speaking.

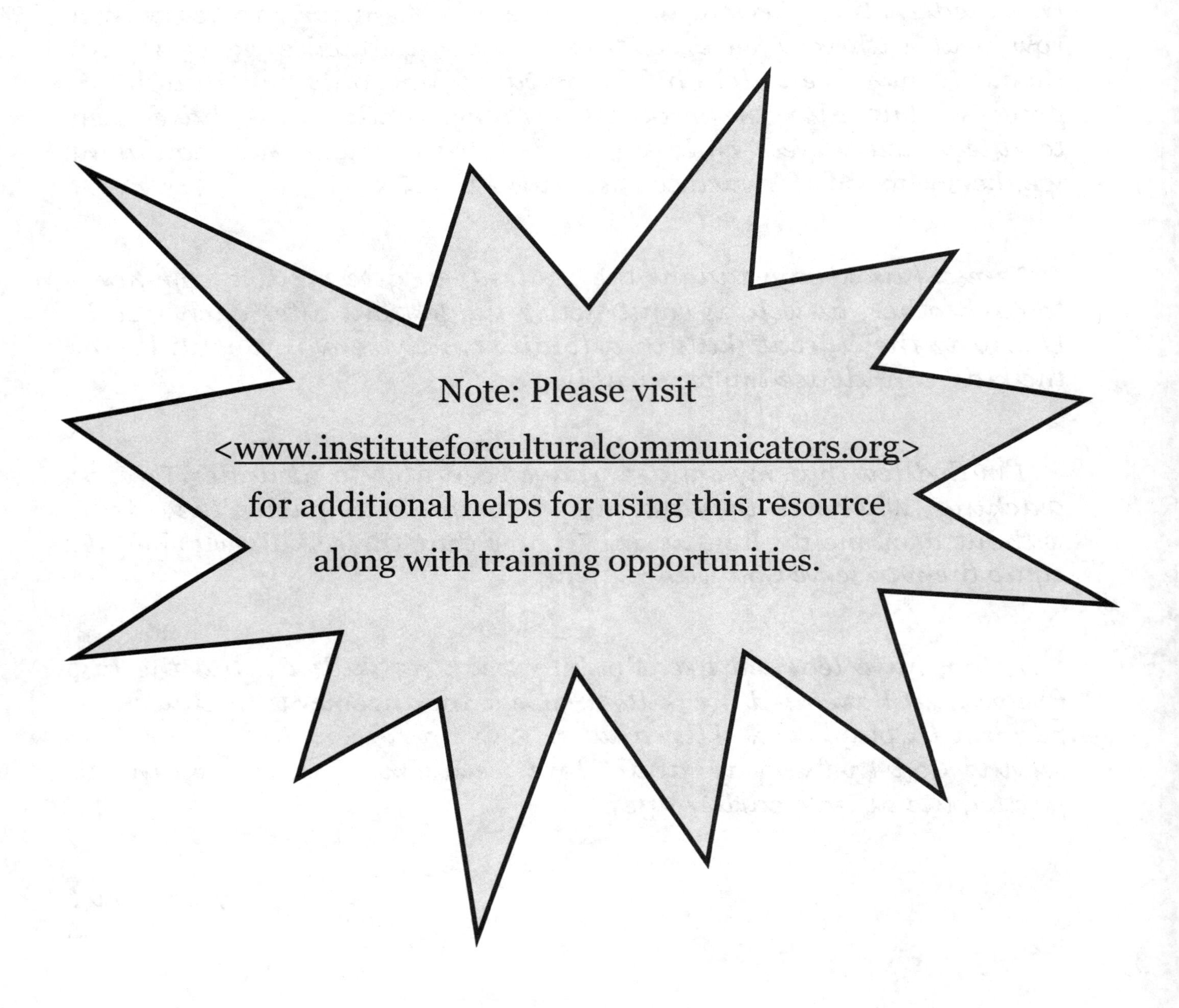
Note: Please visit
<www.instituteforculturalcommunicators.org>
for additional helps for using this resource
along with training opportunities.

Orientation Class Meeting

"People don't care how much we know until they know how much we care."

Be pleasant
and hold their interest
when you speak the message.
Choose your words carefully
and be ready to give answers
to anyone who asks questions.

Colossians 4:6

The Learning Bible
Contemporary English Version

Dear Speaker,

A long, long time ago—back when I was a "kid"—my mom would make me give speeches for large audiences. Actually, at first I gave them for small audiences, like you will be doing. Then came larger audiences. Oh, how I hated it! I couldn't get over the fact that I was pretty much the only eight year old I knew who had to participate in public speaking! Now, here I am, over a decade later, and I can't think of anything better to do with my time than accept the privilege of the platform. Looking in retrospect, I couldn't thank my mom enough for making me do what I at one time dreaded.

As much as I want to believe that my mother was actually pitying me as I was speaking to audiences of hundreds, I really don't think she was. She thought it was a great idea! I understand that I can't ever empathize with what my mom went through just to get me on a stage, let alone to look comfortable and communicate clearly up there. Oh, what my parents wouldn't give to have had this public speaking curriculum fifteen years ago, or, better yet, when *they* were kids.

I have recently discovered that my role throughout my mother's public speaking career was a benefit to her. I was a guinea pig. I concede that it's not my favorite role, but someone has to play it. As one of the earliest guinea pigs for the very public speaking curriculum you will be using for the next several weeks or months, I can tell you if this curriculum worked on *me* over a decade ago, I believe wholeheartedly that it will be most effective for YOU. So, start now to do what I finally did: dive in, enjoy yourself, and have a great time! This class could very well be one of the most enjoyable and useful things you will do in your life.

Devin Moon

Growing up, Devin was a student in this very BPS course more than 15 times! He has now taught these skills in more than 30 states, becoming the most experienced instructor ICC has ever had. He is a nationally ranked speaker and is recognized as a coach all over the United States and a few other countries. Devin has spoken for Toastmasters, groups of realtors, schools of martial arts, public schools in China and groups in Switzerland, Holland, Egypt, and Brazil. Proving that speakers can be strong in both body and mind, Devin holds a Second Degree Black Belt and National Championship titles in the martial art of Tae Kwon Do. At the time of this printing, he is Co-Executive Producer for a television series in Brazil that communicates relevant Christian messages through Brazilian media.

Class Meeting #1

"People don't care how much we know until they know how much we care."

What is Public Speaking?

Public: "In general, the word 'public' expresses something common to humankind at large; to a nation, state, city or town; and is opposed to private, which denotes what belongs to an individual, family, company" (*Dictionary of the American English Language*, 1828, Noah Webster).

Speak: "To express thoughts by words; to talk; to express opinions; to dispute; to discourse; to pronounce; to utter articulately; to declare; to proclaim; to talk or converse in; as in conversation; to communicate" (*Dictionary of the American English Language,* 1828, Noah Webster).

- What makes public speaking "public"?
- How large does the audience have to be? Who is in the audience?
- How do you speak differently in public than you do in private? Is there a difference in delivery? In content?
- What do we use, in addition to words, to communicate feelings? What if you are giving directions? How do you express needs? How do you communicate in emergencies?
- Why do we need to understand and practice public speaking skills?
- Give some examples of people who have a career in public speaking.
- How do you think you will use the skills of public speaking in your own life?

SPEAKER RESPONSIBILITIES

Use this page to record important points made as your classmates critique your speeches. Then refer back to these points when you are practicing speeches.

. . . THINK ABOUT YOUR AUDIENCE . . .

ALWAYS	NEVER
☺ Smile	☹ Frown
☺ Speak Clearly	☹ Mumble
☺ Prepare	☹ Make Excuses
☺ ______	☹ ______
☺ ______	☹ ______
☺ ______	☹ ______
☺ ______	☹ ______

Things to Remember . . .

____

____

____

____

____

____

____

____

____

Public Speaking Quiz

***ASSIGNMENT**: This quiz is due during Class Meeting #8. Review the questions between class meetings and ask about those you need help answering.*

1. What is *public speaking*? (10 points)

2. When and where does public speaking take place? (10 points)

3. Who can you think of that uses public speaking in his/her job? (10 points)

4. Name four types of speeches. Give the purpose of each, and describe a setting in which it might be useful. (40 points)

   1)

   2)

   3)

   4)

5) List as many characteristics of a well-delivered speech as you can. (10 points)

6) How are you most likely going to use public speaking in your life? (10 points)

Bonus: What does it mean to you to be a *Communicator for Christ*? (10 points)

PRESENTATION

IMPROMPTU SPEAKING INTRODUCTIONS

(Impromptu: spontaneous; unplanned; on the spot)

Use the following notes to give an Impromptu Speaking speech to your small group. Try to show your audience that you are thinking about them.

Share:

- ❖ Your name
- ❖ Your birthday
- ❖ Your grade in school
- ❖ Your favorite school subject
- ❖ Your favorite thing to do in your free time
- ❖ Your favorite type of food and your favorite place to eat it

3-Second Rule

Once on the platform and ___________ you start ___________, you should take your place, and_______ to _________ in your ___________.

At the _____ of your speech, you should ________ to _________ in ________ _______ again _____________ you go back to your ___________.

Dear Speaker,

My brother Johnny has three elegant Ninja swords, sheathed in red with dragon-shaped handles, displayed in our living room. Imagine that a real Ninja came to our house one day, looking as though he meant to do us harm. How do you think Johnny would feel if we put one of his swords in his hand, bidding him to save us from the evil Ninja?! Might he be nervous? Terrified?

This is exactly how I felt years ago when Mom told me that I'd be speaking the next day in front of a Toastmasters audience. I felt exactly as though she'd asked me to fight a Ninja. There was no way anyone could make me speak with people quietly staring at me! But think about Johnny, if he were to apprentice himself to a Ninja, working studiously and strenuously, and then the same situation were to come up with the evil Ninja, do you think he might feel differently? Might he be bold? Confident?

Similarly, three years ago I became a public speaking apprentice. When the time came that I had to speak for an audience, I felt wonderfully confident, and I was able to convey my message with clarity because it wasn't tangled up with my fear. If you feel nervous right now about public speaking, you're normal. You expected Johnny to be nervous, fighting with no experience, right? Of course! He hadn't learned how to do it!

I invite *you* to learn to use the sword of public speaking!

Because, unlike having to fight a Ninja, public speaking is something we all have to do at some point in our lives. Something as simple as standing up at church to give directions to your house is "public speaking." If you're nervous, that's okay, it's normal; but don't worry, you *can* overcome it. To be afraid and to be brave is the best courage of all. Go forth and fight your Ninja!

Jessie McLean

A three-time national speech competitor, Jessie has earned a great deal of recognition for her ability to command the public platform. In addition to her competitive accomplishments, Jessie has spoken for many diverse audiences including the Forty-and-Eight Club for Veterans, the American Legion Post, and the Exchange Club. She has taught speakers and debaters across the US and in the Philippines. She is currently a student at Cedarville University where she is majoring in Graphic Design.

ASSIGNMENT

Reading or Recitation

Prepare to read or recite a short story or poem. Your reading or recitation needs to meet the following requirements:

- Presentation should be one-half to one-minute in length.
- Selection must be appropriate to share with an audience of all ages.
- Be prepared to present at the **beginning** of class.

Your in-class reading or recitation will be evaluated for the following criteria:

- Use of the 3-Second Rule
- Making Eye contact
- Projection (how loud and soft you are)
- Inflection (making your voice interesting)
- Appropriate selection for the audience
- Staying within the time allotted
  (You will be stopped if you go over one minute.)

Class Meeting #2

"People don't care
how much we know
until they know
how much we care."

AUDIENCE ROLE

The audience should be thinking about the Speaker________.

Ways to encourage the speaker **during** the presentation:

- Eye contact
- sit still
- be Patiant

At the **end** of the presentation, the audience Clap + Aplaude________.

This is to show:

- your listening
- Paying attention
- not fiddling

The purpose of giving a speaker feedback (critique) after his/her speech in this setting is. . .

- We are all here to learn how to make speeches.
- We all want to learn it.
- General feedback like "bad" or "great" is not helpful because ________
  ____
  ____.
- The most helpful critiques are ____________ and ____________.

MOST IMPORTANT PUBLIC SPEAKING TIPS

Listen for these *Important Public Speaking Tips* as you go through class. They are key tips for any public speaking situation and you will want to use them throughout the rest of this class. Post them in a place where you will remember to review them as you practice your presentations.

❖ Think about ____________ and not about ______________________.

❖ Use the _____ ___________ Rule at the ___________ and _______ of each speech.

❖ Look at _____________ __________________. It makes them feel (___ ________). This is called making ______________.

❖ **P**______ is a very important skill. It means that if something goes wrong you ________ _______.

❖ Show your audience you are excited about sharing with them by wearing a ___________.

Reading & Recitation Evaluation

SPEAKER NAME:	TITLE:				
Beginning and Ending with Confidence **(3-Second Rule)**	**1**	**2**	**3**	**4**	**5**
Pronouncing Words Well **(Articulation and Enunciation)**	**1**	**2**	**3**	**4**	**5**
Volume **(Louder & Softer)**	**1**	**2**	**3**	**4**	**5**
Eye Contact	**1**	**2**	**3**	**4**	**5**
Expression	**1**	**2**	**3**	**4**	**5**
Comments:					

MY OWN READING AND RECITATION EVALUATION

I DID WELL IN THESE PARTS OF MY SPEECH:

1. ______________________________

____

2. ______________________________

____

NEXT TIME I AM GOING TO WORK ON IMPROVING:

1. ______________________________

____

INFORMATIVE SPEAKING ACTIVITY

PAPER TEARING

Tear a piece of paper into a shape that tells your audience something about you.

Think of an object that represents:

- Your personality

- Your favorite hobby
- Something you believe or feel strongly about
- A special talent
- Something about your family

Tear the paper into this shape the best you can.

Prepare to share what your shape stands for and why you chose to use it. Use as many interesting details as you can in sharing your object.

NOTE: "Expository" and "Informative" are both names of speeches to inform.
This curriculum is using these names interchangeably.

Topics I Would Like to Talk About in an Informative Speech

My Informative Speech Notes

ADDITIONAL INFORMATIVE/EXPOSITORY SPEAKING ACTIVITY

Try at home this week.

WHAT ARE YOU?

- Think of an object to describe to the group (or to your family).
- Tell only your group leader (or parent) what your object is.
- Now, act as if you are your object and prepare to describe it in the first person.
- Describe yourself to the group using as many details as possible.
- Try to tell how you look, feel, smell, taste, sound, etc.
- Keep talking until the group is able to guess your object.

"A picture paints a thousand words."

INFORMATIVE SPEECH

(EXPOSITORY)

. . . *WITH* VISUAL AIDS

An Expository or Informative Speech is one that informs your audience about something you are interested in. Prepare an *Informative Speech ... with Visual Aids.* Talk about a topic with which you are familiar. It might be a sport, hobby, or something you enjoy doing in your free time. You might choose to talk about a favorite person you have studied or a book you have read. Bring a picture, chart, poster or prop to help your audience relate to your topic. Practice using your visual aid(s) in your speech. Be sure to include where you got your information (book title, authors, experts, events, teachers, etc.).

Requirements:

- One to two minutes in length
- Factual - - this is not something you make up
- Include an appropriate visual aid(s)

Your speech will be evaluated for:

- Interesting details
- Organization
- Preparation
- Eye contact
- Articulation
- Beginning and ending with confidence
  or using the 3-Second Rule

Ideas for my speech:

- My favorite school subject
- Sports I play
- Music lessons/my musical instrument
- Hobbies
- Family recreation
- My mom's or dad's career
- A subject I have read a lot about

Dear Speaker,

In a land far away, also known as Louisiana, lived a young girl who was simply minding her own business. Unexpectedly, her mother informed her that she had just signed up her daughter for a class. The girl asked curiously, "What kind of class are you talking about, Mom?"

Her mom explained to her that it was a class that taught you how to speak in front of people. Taken back by what she thought was a horrible idea, she responded (arms folded in defiance), "What! I don't need to learn how to speak in front of people! I'm definitely not going to that class."

A few weeks later, I arrived at my first Communicators for Christ Conference. I decided that I was going to sit in the car until I absolutely had to get out! By the end of that conference, my perspective towards public speaking began to change. To my surprise, I actually had a lot of fun! I realized that my parents were right, and that, while learning to speak in front of people may not always be that comfortable, it is a necessary skill to learn.

In closing, I would like to tell you that whether you're 6 or 60, God has given you a message to share with others. Although you might be afraid at first, as you continue to practice, you will become an excellent communicator of the message that God has given you.

Erin Cromer

Erin has earned top awards in local and state speech competitions. She has spoken for local churches, speech classes, the VFW, and parent-teacher meetings. Erin has coached fellow public speakers, led a teen Bible study, and taught Sunday school in her local church. She has a heart for missions, enjoys travelling, and loves her family. Her real passion is to teach her generation to use their communication skills to influence people for Christ. She currently attends Louisiana State University.

Class Meeting #3

"People don't care how much we know until they know how much we care."

Share or model right and wrong ways to address a group. Here are a few things not to do. What are some others?

- Beginning . . . "This is dumb . . ." or "I really don't want to give this speech."
- Chewing gum
- Not making eye contact
- mammbling
- go off topic
- hands in pockets
-
-
-
-

If the above behaviors distract from the presentation, what behaviors will enhance the presentation? Here are a few ideas. Can you think of more?

- Begin with confidence (3-Second Rule)
- Fluctuate speaking voice (inflections)
- Speak loudly, but "normally" or appropriately
- NEVER, NEVER, NEVER QUIT
- DON'T CHEW GUM
- Make eye contact
- be rude
-
-

You are not expected to master all of these at one time. You will focus on a different aspect of public speaking each week. It would be good to add to this list later. It should help you review some important things to think about when you practice.

Informative/Expository Speech . . . with Visual Aids Evaluation

SPEAKER NAME:					
Interesting Details	1	2	3	4	5
Organization	1	2	3	4	5
Preparation	1	2	3	4	5
Eye Contact	1	2	3	4	5
Articulation	1	2	3	4	5
Beginning and Ending with Confidence (3-Second Rule)	1	2	3	4	5
Comment:					

INFORMATIVE/EXPOSITORY SPEAKING ACTIVITY

Have fun doing this at home this week.

<u>WHAT'S IN MY POCKET?</u>

Unlike the familiar game "Twenty Questions," the goal of this game is **NOT** to ask <u>**yes**</u> or <u>**no**</u> questions, but to ask questions which are worded to solicit as much information as possible.

- Each questioner gets one question and one opportunity to guess per turn.
- Once a questioner guesses incorrectly, he/she is out until the next game.

USING HUMOR IN PUBLIC SPEAKING

PREPARE TO TELL A JOKE OR FUNNY STORY TO THE CLASS.

THINGS TO THINK ABOUT . . .

- Practice your joke or story so that you can tell it all the way through without mixing anything up.
- A narrative is better than a "knock-knock" joke or riddle.
- Practice saying the punch line correctly, without laughing.
- Be sure your joke is appropriate.
- Use pauses to make your joke-telling more effective.
- Think of an original beginning.
- Memorize your joke completely, no notes or cue cards.

CRITERIA . . .

Your joke will be evaluated for:

- Use of time
- Appropriate theme
- Beginning and ending with confidence (3-Second Rule)
- Articulation
- Appropriate expression, gestures, pauses
- Eye contact

Remember: We use humor and funny stories to delight our audience. An offended audience will NOT be delighted.

Dear Speaker,

I *love* baseball. I played for 12 years and loved every minute of it -- even practice! In fact, I practiced *all* the time. I used to wake up early in the morning, put one some gym clothes, run outside and do baseball drills. Then, in the afternoon, I would meet up with the baseball team and practice some more. And then in my spare time I would hang out with some of the other players on the team to play even more! To say the least, I practiced a lot.

So why did I spend so much time practicing? I wanted to do my absolute best when I was in the game. Doing well in the big, exciting moments made all my effort worth it. And this was how I viewed my communication practice too - something that I would develop and use when the important "game time" scenarios came my way. But communication isn't like baseball. We can't develop these skills and then save them for when we're on a platform talking to hundreds of people. In communication, "game time" is *all* the time.

As Christians, we are always Christ's representative, no matter where we are -- giving a presentation on the public platform, hanging out with friends, or just spending time with family. While we can (and should!) practice and refine our communications skills, we need to be aware that God wants us to use what we've learned *all* day *every* day to bring his truth to the world.

John David McLean

John David McLean is a charter member of the Young Speakers' Guild. As a Chapter member, he has had the privilege and pleasure of speaking on a variety of public platforms, including libraries, political rallies, and schools. He especially enjoys using the skills he has learned to train other Christians to become winsome and articulate communicators. In 2010, he had the opportunity to be an instructor on the ICC IMPACT Singapore team, where he and 11 others spoke to several organizations on becoming effective communicators for Christ. He looks forward to applying his communications skills by pursuing his college education in public policy.

Class Meeting #4

"People don't care how much we know until they know how much we care."

Evaluating Speaking Skills

Two major areas on which we can focus to improve oral presentations are:

______________________ **and** ______________________.

Delivery Skills include:

- ______________________
- ______________________
- ______________________
- ______________________
- ______________________
- ______________________
- ______________________
- ______________________
- ______________________
- ______________________

Content Skills include:

- ______________________
- ______________________
- ______________________

- ______________________
- ______________________
- ______________________

- ______________________
- ______________________

HUMOROUS INTERPRETATION
EVALUATION

SPEAKER NAME:					
Time (Maximum: 2 minutes)	1	2	3	4	5
Appropriate Theme	1	2	3	4	5
Beginning and Ending with Confidence (3-Second Rule)	1	2	3	4	5
Articulation	1	2	3	4	5
Appropriate Expressions, Gestures, Pauses	1	2	3	4	5
Eye Contact	1	2	3	4	5
Comment:					

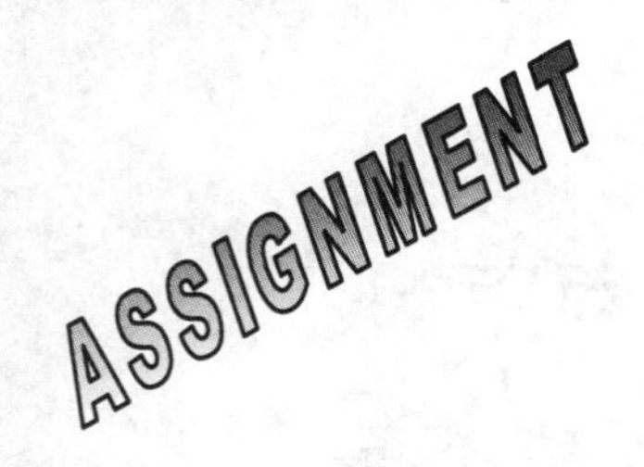

Impromptu Speaking Topics for All Ages

<u>Note</u>: Parents, you can help your children learn to think on their feet! Use these topics to help them practice Impromptu Speaking.

Purpose

To practice responding to questions or statements using one or more examples like the following to develop a point: a personal experience, a historical event, a story from literature, a current event.

Practice

Select a topic from this list to practice your limited preparation speaking (impromptu) skills. You will be given sixty seconds to think about making a point on this topic. Then you will speak about it for one to two minutes. Someone should give you time signals during this activity so you know how long you are thinking and how long you are speaking. Then do it again!

My birthday . . .

Christmas at our house . . .

My favorite family time was when . . .

Easter is . . .

Thanksgiving means . . .

A good education is important because . . .

One way to show Christian love and care to my brother or sister is . . .

The best book I ever read was . . . (Tell why.)

If I could meet anyone in the world it would be . . . (Tell why.)

If I had the chance to speak to the whole world at one time, I would say . . .

If I could go anywhere I wanted to just once, it would be . . . (Tell why.)

If I suddenly inherited a million dollars I would . . .

My favorite season of the year is . . .

Public Speaking is an important skill because . . .

Dear Speaker,

Little Jimmy sat at his desk, furiously scribbling on a piece of paper. Other students looked on with wonder as his paper began to fill with the product of his brilliance. The numbers came swift and sure--until Jimmy made one fatal misstep. Four and two does not, in fact, equal eight.

As this unfortunate fact of mathematics dawned upon him, the teacher prepared for what was coming next. Little Jimmy's eyes filled with tears of rage as he shouted: "WHY DO WE NEED TO LEARN THIS STUFF ANYWAY?????"

Just as my mom answered every time I asked this question, Jimmy's teacher responded with a variation on the "life skills for the future" theme that proves so true. Now that I'm older and SO much wiser, I have another question for my mom, and any teachers who may be reading this: Just how many times have YOU used the Pythagorean theorem in the past week?

OK, I really do understand that math is important. Think about it honestly--how many people actually use anything beyond basic arithmetic in their daily lives? Yet, these skills are considered important enough to be taught in every school in every country around the world.

So when it comes to learning public speaking, I must ask the obvious question: how many times have you talked to someone over the past week? If math skills are so very important, even though we don't actually use most of them, how much more important is it to learn to communicate? Beyond just opening doors for you, and earning you interviews and job opportunities later in life, being able to communicate your thoughts will give you the confidence you need to succeed at every task--whether as a CEO, a fighter pilot, or by teaching future generations the value of education. Yes, even *math* education.

Elizabeth Kays

Elizabeth travelled as a CFC intern in 2005 and currently serves as ICC's Director of International Events. She has taught communication to students all across the US and co-directed summer camps for speakers and debaters. At this printing, she is in her final year of studying Chemistry at Oxford University, and she plans to remain in the UK and train as an attorney. She enjoys using her communication skills to analyze, write about, and discuss theology, science, and culture from a Christian perspective.

CLASS MEETING #5

"People don't care

how much we know

until they know

how much we care."

Impromptu Speaking Activity

Impromptu: spontaneous; unplanned; on the spot

There are many opportunities for giving impromptu speeches. You may be called on in meetings of clubs and organizations. You could find yourself addressing a need in church or school with little or no planning. Whatever the situation, it helps to remember good public speaking skills in order to communicate with your audience.

Directions for this Impromptu Speaking Activity:

1. Draw your topic.
2. Timer will begin timing as soon as you draw.
3. You have one minute to think about the topic.
4. You will have one to two minutes to speak about the topic.
5. Goal: respond to questions or statements using one or more examples such as the following to develop a point: a personal experience, a historical event, a story from literature, a current event.

Especially concentrate on the following speaking skills:

(Use this list as a guideline for your own speech and to critique the speeches of those in your group.)

- Developing a point
- Organization of thought
- Illustrations, stories, interesting details

Impromptu Speaking Critique

SPEAKER NAME:	TOPIC/TITLE:

Components of the Speech	Points Possible	Points Given
BEGINNING AND ENDING WITH CONFIDENCE ("3-Second Rule")	15	
POISE	15	
EYE CONTACT	15	
ILLUSTRATIONS, STORIES, INTERESTING DETAILS	15	
ORGANIZATION	15	
ARTICULATION	15	
VOLUME, PROJECTION	10	
TOTAL POINTS EARNED	100	

Comments:

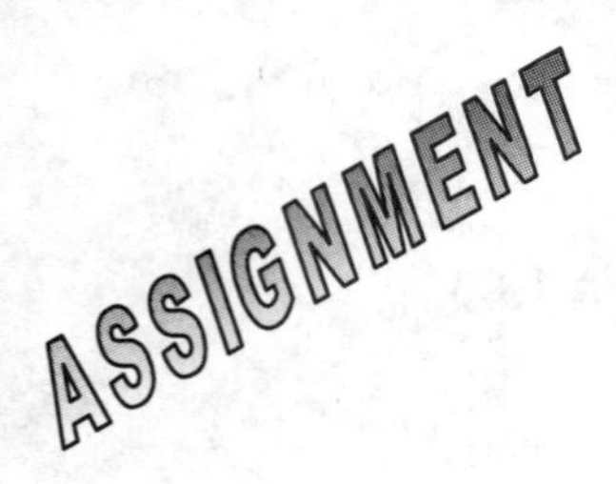

SPEECH ON A *CURRENT EVENT*
EXTEMPORANEOUS

Think of an issue that is currently in the news.
Prepare to relate the details of the issue to your group.

In a well-organized presentation, try to answer as many of the following questions as you can:

- Why is this an important issue in our world today?
- Who does it affect?
- What makes this issue newsworthy?
- Does the media report this issue from a bias? What is the media's bias? Can you think of a media source that reports from a different bias?
- Do you have a solution to the problem presented in the news story? What is your solution?
- How or why is your solution better than those proposed by the media?

Current Event Speeches will be critiqued for the following characteristics:

- Selection of a newsworthy issue
- Interesting details
- Substance: Real information and facts about the issue
- Organization of information (*Current Event Speech Outline* may help you)
- Beginning and ending with confidence (3-Second Rule)
- Poise
- Eye contact

Issues in the News

ISSUES IN THE NEWS

ASSIGNMENT

Current Event Speech Outline

There are several ways to organize your speech. When you don't have much time to prepare, and you have several important things to say, it is good to have an organization into which you can put your ideas. It's a little bit like a pattern. You just fit the points you want to make into the pattern. This one is a Problem-Solution Speech. It is very important that your audience be able to follow your ideas throughout your speech.

I. Introduction

II. The Issue

A. The Problem *(Describe the problem in your own words.)*

1.

2.

B. The Importance of the Problem *(Tell why you think it is in the news.)*

1.

2.

III. The Solution(s)

A. Present a solution(s) to the problem
(These can be the solutions proposed in the news or your own solution(s).)

1.

2.

B. Compare and Contrast Proposed Solutions
(If there is more than one solution, compare them.)

1.

2.

IV. Conclusion:

Restate the problem, the possible solutions, and your recommended solution.

Dear Speaker,

About three years ago I decided I would try Impromptu Speaking. It was mostly my mom's idea (which I hear is common). I signed up to compete in Impromptu at a small contest. A few days before the event where I was to speak, my mom made me practice my first ever Impromptu Speech, and it was an awful, horrible, and rotten speech. I wasn't sure what to say, and so I mumbled through it, while my dog sat on the kitchen floor and listened.

I started to get a little worried about Impromptu Speaking. It was one thing giving an embarrassing speech for my mom and my dog, they would love me anyway (the mom because she's a mom, and the dog because I feed it) but who knows what strangers or friends would think of me if I gave a horrible speech for them. I had a nightmare. In my nightmare, I got up to give my speech, looked at my audience, and fell to the floor with a thud. I had fainted. I woke up and wished with all my heart that I would not have to give an Impromptu Speech, and that the day of the competition would never come.

Being scared of something doesn't make it stop coming though. My mom woke me up early one morning, while it was still dark, and we drove to the contest. When I arrived at the contest I didn't faint, but I sure wished I would when they called my name to speak. I got up there, and was surprised to find I had something to say! Not much, but something. I gave two Impromptu Speeches that day, and by the end of the day I was still alive. I lived so that I could find out that I did NOT win the contest.

As I practiced Impromptu Speeches more and more, I decided I really didn't like Impromptu. I knew it wouldn't kill me, but torture is always a concern for me. I decided I just wasn't good at Impromptu. I also decided that I might just give up.

Then one day, I realized that I should practice Impromptu Speaking, even if I didn't like it. You see, God says we need to be ready to tell people about the hope we have as Christians. I decided that one way to be ready was to practice speaking confidently and thinking fast in hard situations. Impromptu Speaking was one of those hard situations for me.

For the past three years God has helped me work on my Impromptu Speaking skills. I can think more quickly and speak more confidently than I ever could before. I've even learned that Impromptu can be fun sometimes, and I've won some Impromptu Speaking contests. I did all of that because God told me I shouldn't give up, and He helped me to be brave enough to keep giving Impromptu Speeches. Thanks to Him, I don't dream about fainting before I give an Impromptu Speech anymore.

Michele Hop

Michele lives on the grounds of a youth camp in New Albany, IN, where she and her family are janitors, counselors, activity leaders, cooks, and entertainers. Michele, herself a national award-winning speaker and debater, enjoys coaching other communicators to impact their culture with the light of Christ. She has addressed a wide variety of audiences, including firemen, literature clubs, Toastmasters and retirement communities. Michele served as a CFC intern in 2006 and studies Journalism at Indiana SE. As of this printing, she is preparing to spend a year travelling across the globe using her communication skills to share truth, hope, and grace.

CLASS MEETING #6

"People don't care
how much we know
until they know
how much we care."

ORAL INTERPRETATION

WORKING COPY

Books I have read that have *Scenes* I would like to *Interpret*.

DRAMATIC	HUMOROUS

Current Event Speech Critique

Speaker Name:	Topic/Title:

Components of the Speech	Points Possible	Points Given
SELECTION OF A NEWSWORTHY ISSUE	20	
USE OF INTERESTING DETAILS	15	
SUBSTANCE	15	
ORGANIZATION	15	
BEGINNING AND ENDING WITH CONFIDENCE ("3-SECOND RULE")	15	
EYE CONTACT	10	
POISE	10	
TOTAL POINTS EARNED	100	

Comments:

ASSIGNMENT

ORAL INTERPRETATION

DRAMATIC/HUMOROUS

Length

Maximum two to three minutes

Topic

Any well-written prose or poetry that lends itself to drama or humor

Suggested Resources

- Excerpts from children's literature
- Poetry – humorous or serious
- Scripture verses
- A short story
-
-
-
-

Presentation will be critiqued for . . .

- Selection of material
- Expression
- Appropriate gestures
- Variety in presentation (including volume, expression, tone of voice . . .)

Helpful Hints

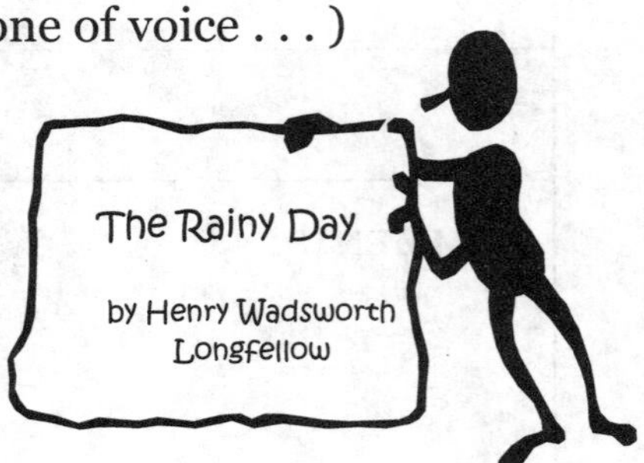

This speech *should be* presented word for word. You may edit the text by cutting portions, but do not change the author's wording. The shorter the piece, the more expression you will find you are able to include.

Copy the speech and paste or tape it onto heavy construction paper or tag board. Read it enough times to memorize it if possible, or at least to get as close as you can.

Oral Interpretation

FINAL COPY

Books I have read that have *Scenes* I would like to *Interpret*.

Dramatic	*Humorous*
______________________________	______________________________
______________________________	______________________________
______________________________	______________________________
______________________________	______________________________
______________________________	______________________________
______________________________	______________________________
______________________________	______________________________
______________________________	______________________________
______________________________	______________________________
______________________________	______________________________
______________________________	______________________________
______________________________	______________________________
______________________________	______________________________
______________________________	______________________________

TESTIMONIALS

I'm so glad I took the Beginning Public Speaking class. I didn't know public speaking could be this much fun!

Caleb (7) LA

My favorite kind of speech is Expository. I like showing people all of my animals.

~Tristen (11) NH

My favorite public speaking tip is "poise." It's important to keep going when something goes wrong.

~Cory (9) RI

I wish the public speaking class was longer. It's already over and I was just starting to like it.

~Ashley (8) IN

My favorite public speaking tip is the 3-Second Rule. I think it helps to count to three at the beginning and end of my speech.

~Charity (10) WI

My favorite speech is Impromptu. It's always fun to try to think of something to say.

~Trey (9) NC

I think everyone should take a public speaking class!

~Anthony (11) TN

My favorite part of this school year was the public speaking program. My grandma and grandpa came, and my mom and dad, and my sisters. I gave my Dr. Seuss speech and it was the best!

~Victoria (10) PA

I can't wait to do public speaking again!

~Katie (8) CA

In my first speech I cried. I told my mom I didn't want to do it. Now I like it and I can't wait to come back. I think public speaking is my favorite class.

~Jordan (10) MS

Issues about which I would like to persuade other people.

Class Meeting #7

"People don't care

how much we know

until they know

how much we care."

Oral Interpretation Critique

Speaker Name:	Topic/Title:

Components of the Speech	Points Possible	Points Given
SELECTION OF MATERIAL	15	
EXPRESSION	15	
POISE	10	
APPROPRIATE GESTURES	10	
EYE CONTACT	10	
ARTICULATION	10	
VARIETY IN PRESENTATION (VOLUME, TONE OF VOICE, MOVEMENT)	15	
BEGINNING AND ENDING WITH CONFIDENCE ("3-SECOND RULE")	15	
TOTAL POINTS EARNED	100	

Comments:

ASSIGNMENT

PERSUASIVE ORATORY

Think of something about which you have very strong feelings. This may be any type of issue that is appropriate to discuss in a public setting.

Suggestions:

- Your personal faith
- Your form of education
- Types of recreation
- Health & nutrition
- Exercise
- Respect
- Honoring your parents
- Community service
- Bible study, devotion
- Friendships
- Family
- Government
- Legislative issues
- Types of music
- Missionary service

Tell why this issue matters to you. . .

- How it affects your life and the lives of people you know.
- How you want people to think or behave differently about this issue.
- Tell what you are persuading the audience to do.
- Give means to do what you are asking (phone numbers, web address, and other resources).

Time Limit: Maximum two to three minutes.

You will be critiqued for:

- Interesting details
- Organization
- Poise
- Eye contact
- Articulation
- Persuasiveness
- Expression
- Use of time

Note: *This speech ought to demonstrate everything you have learned so far about public speaking. Pay attention to both content and delivery skills. Review your notes from this class as you prepare this last speech.*

My Persuasive Speaking Notes:

Dear Speaker,

Lucy Pevensie walked into a magic wardrobe and found an enchanted world, complete with evil queens, fauns, talking animals, and *snow*! Wouldn't you like to find a magical world like that - just by stepping through a door?

Well, you can! I know because I did it two years ago. It wasn't a *wardrobe* door I walked through. It was a door to a classroom. I didn't meet a faun or find a lamppost in an enchanted wintry forest - in fact, the world I entered seemed pretty commonplace at first, with desks, a chalkboard, and hard metal chairs. But from that moment on, I've been on an adventure. What adventure? The adventure of a *lifetime*. The adventure that we *all* must take as Christians: the adventure of changing the world by communicating for *Christ!*

You see, the magical door I had walked through was the door to my first speech class, the door to a magical world of communication. Like Lucy, I was a bit frightened at first. You probably know that speaking in front of people isn't always easy! But the lessons I learned there - like the gifts Lucy got from Father Christmas - have become tools of victory in an ongoing battle! I've learned how important words are: we speak them every day! I've also learned that we must learn to use our words to complete *Jesus'* will - we *must* learn to communicate for Christ.

You can step through a doorway into a magical land, just like I did. As you begin a new journey of learning how to *communicate*, I know you are in for *adventure*. Though it might seem scary now, you'll soon discover what fun this magical place can be. And, like Lucy, you'll find your place in it - speaking the words Jesus gives you, to battle the evil forces of this world and communicate for the King!!

So come into the wardrobe....

Hannah Vanbiber

Hannah is a national award-winning speaker and debater. She has entertained, informed, and persuaded audiences on a variety of community platforms including Right to Life, youth events, teen purity seminars, and father-daughter banquets. She was a CFC Intern in 2006, and has taught communication skills to conference participants across the country. At this printing, Hannah is studying abroad and will return to complete her degree in English (Pre-Law) at Covenant College.

Class Meeting #8

"People don't care

how much we know

until they know

how much we care."

PERSUASIVE ORATORY CRITIQUE

SPEAKER NAME:	TOPIC/TITLE:

COMPONENTS OF THE SPEECH	POINTS POSSIBLE	POINTS GIVEN
USE OF INTERESTING DETAILS	10	
ORGANIZATION	15	
POISE	10	
PERSUASIVENESS	25	
EYE CONTACT	10	
ARTICULATION	10	
EXPRESSION	10	
BEGINNING AND ENDING WITH CONFIDENCE ("3-SECOND RULE")	10	
TOTAL POINTS EARNED	100	

COMMENTS:

Public Speaking Quiz

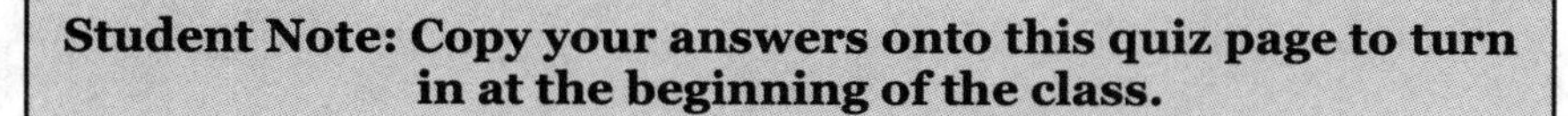

1. What is *public speaking*? (10 points)

2. When and where does public speaking take place? (10 points)

3. Who can you think of that uses public speaking in his/her job? (10 points)

4. Name four types of speeches. Give the purpose of each, and describe a setting in which it might be useful. (40 points)

    1)

    2)

    3)

    4)

5. List as many characteristics of a well-delivered speech as you can. (10 points)

6. How are you most likely going to use public speaking in your life? (10 points)

Bonus: What does it mean to you to be a *Communicator for Christ*? (10 points)

Additional Notes:

Dear Speaker,

I had one thought as I sat in my very first speech class: "Toto, I have a feeling we're not in Kansas anymore!" Like Dorothy from the Wizard of Oz when she first stepped foot into Munchkinland, I was excited, curious, and a little nervous all at once. I also felt lost! I was learning so much about communication that I didn't know where to begin. You may be feeling that same way now - nervous, eager, curious, or feeling suddenly dropped into the middle of it all by a tornado! Either way, don't be afraid to put on your ruby slippers (or if you're a boy, red tennis shoes will do the trick) and begin the journey of public speaking.

As you start walking down the yellow brick road, you'll learn a few things to help you along the way. You'll find out that public speaking isn't easy - that's why you have to practice! I learned that I need to *apply* the things I was taught in order to be a better speaker. Dorothy and her friends learned lessons along the way too. The Lion learned how to have courage to face the Wicked Witch of the West; the Scarecrow learned to use his brain to help rescue his friends; and the Tin-Man realized he did have a heart that cared for other people. But my favorite part about this movie is the fact that the Lion, Scarecrow, Tin-man, and Dorothy didn't need their gifts to be given to them by the Wizard of Oz - no! They HAD those abilities with them the entire time! They just needed to learn how to *find* and *use* them.

The same thing applies to you. You have the ability to courageously step in front of an audience; you have the brains to write a speech; and you have a heart that compassionately cares for other people - all things that God has given you. You just need to learn how to find and develop them in order to communicate for Christ. It will be difficult at times, but you *will* reach the Emerald City of better communication. You *will* be able to "melt" your fears of public speaking, and at the end of your adventure, you'll make it back home safely to communicate to others what you have learned.

All you have to do is take that first step and "follow the yellow brick road!"

Leanne Livingston

Leanne is a charter member of the Young Speakers' Guild. She has applied her public speaking skills in a variety of ways, serving communities both at home and abroad and winning over $6,000 in scholarships. In 2008-2009, she was President of the Sequoyah Regional Library System's Teen Advisory Board. In 2009, as the American Legion Oratorical Contest state champion, she was asked to speak at Memorial and Veteran's Day events alongside members of local government. In 2009-2010, she decided to use her skills to impact the youth of Tullamore, Ireland through a one-year project with Operation Mobilization's Immersion team, teaching religion classes and organizing youth events for a local church. She will return home in June 2010 to work full-time on the campaign of a Georgia gubernatorial candidate.

Class Meeting #9

"People don't care
how much we know
until they know
how much we care."

Dear Speaker,

I started where you are, sitting in a beginning public speaking class and forced to give speeches to friends and strangers. Since then I have spoken to audiences of thousands of people, coached students just like you to speak well, competed in speech and debate in high school and college, ventured to China to communicate hope and truth, and above all, traveled the country several times in a motor home with Communicators for Christ.

Now, all these years later, I look back on these opportunities and recognize that they became possible because of my public speaking preparation. Even though it began as a "you have to ..." from my parents, I appreciate the invaluable tools that I have been able to use every day.

You don't have to wait until you get to college to make an impact through your own communication. Start now by sharing your testimony of faith at Sunday School, write about your favorite family vacation and share it with your family and friends, start a book club and talk with others about your choice of literature or, if you are musically gifted, at your next recital say a few words about the composer of the piece you are performing.

Anytime you are feeling overwhelmed with the daunting task of speaking in front of people remember these words from II Timothy 4:12. *"Don't let anyone look down on you because you are young, but set an example for the believers in speech, in life, in love, in faith and in purity."*

It is no mistake that this scripture passage makes a reference to speech. You have the tools to communicate the most beautiful message in the world, the Truth. Don't let anyone look down on you because you are young, but strive to be an example, beginning with your "speech" and you will become an effective communicator for Christ.

Wendell Moon

At an early age, Wendell told his mom, "My goal in life is to make an audience laugh and cry." Wendell has earned the highest national speech honor awarded to competitors, Sweepstakes Champion, twice while in high school, and again in national college competition. Wendell graduated from Carson-Newman college in 2008 with majors in degree Mass Communications and in Filmmaking. Wendell is dedicated to helping the Institute for Cultural Communicators spread the word with curriculum, literature, web design, and other valuable resources. He is ICC's Director of Media Communications and recently travelled to Brazil where he was co-executive producer of a television series intended to equip local filmmakers to impact their culture with truth through television.

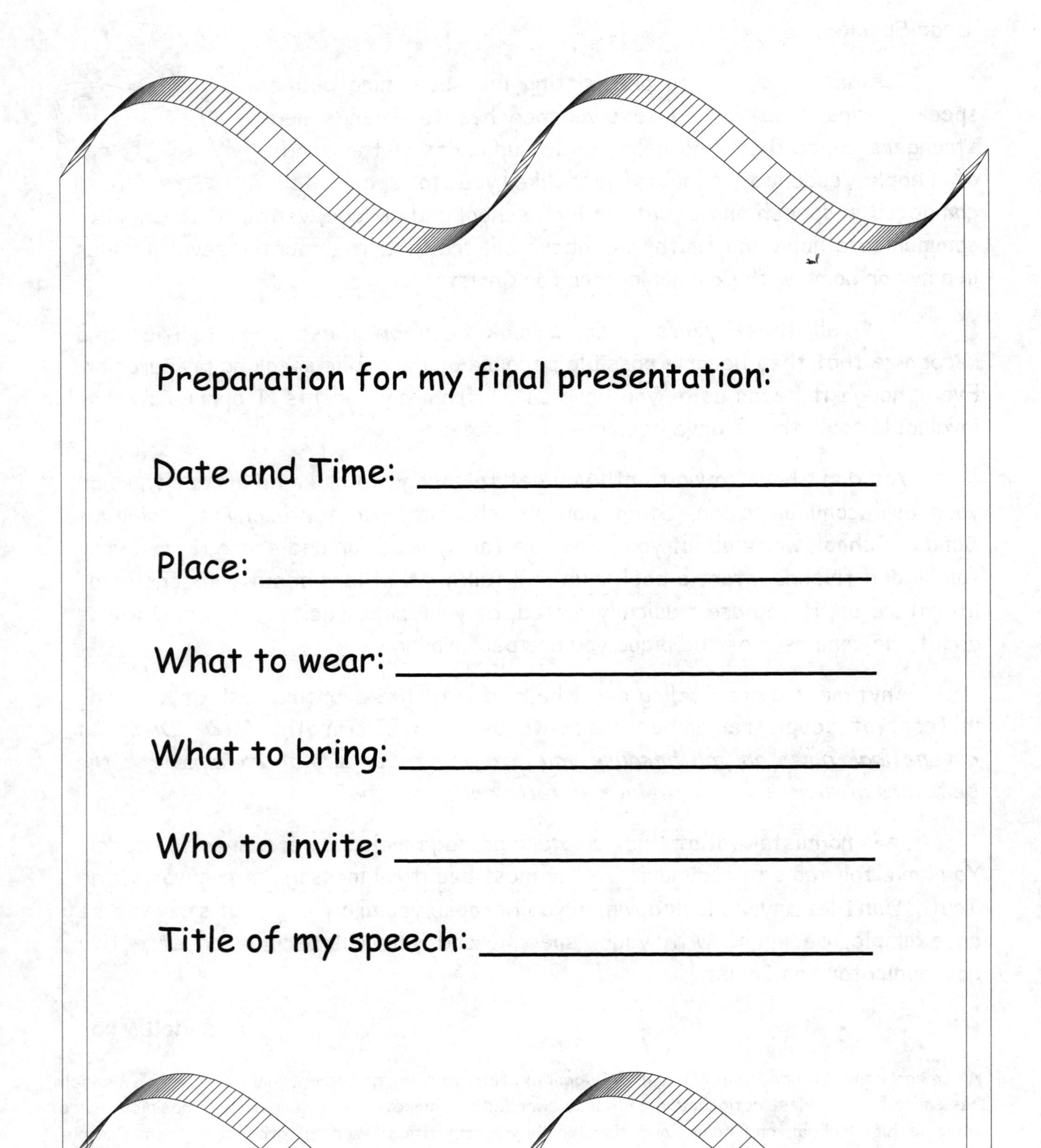
Preparation for my final presentation:

Date and Time: ____________________

Place: ____________________

What to wear: ____________________

What to bring: ____________________

Who to invite: ____________________

Title of my speech: ____________________

Notes about My Final Presentation

The Author

Teresa Moon is a nationally recognized speaker, writer and communication coach for youth across the country and abroad.

She has worked in public, private and home education for 30 years. As an educator, she began to recognize a growing problem: today's youth receive little or no training in basic communication. Moreover, she realized that Christian students lacked the ability to articulate truth effectively with their culture, preventing them from impacting those around them with the truth of Christ. In response, she co-founded and serves as President of the ***Institute for Cultural Communicators***, training students and educators around the world to speak with confidence and passion.

With nearly 16 years of experience in Christian communication education, Teresa is a nationally featured seminar speaker and author of numerous public speaking and debate curricula for students in elementary school all the way through college. She continues to lead a team of student instructors around the country on the annual **Communicators for Christ** Conference Tour, is President and CEO of the **Communicators Advantage Project**, a publishing company, and hosts numerous communication events each year in the US and abroad. She holds Master of Arts degrees in Curriculum/Instruction and Administration and is currently completing doctoral studies at Regent University's School of Global Leadership and Entrepreneurship.

shaping culture through authentic communication

To invite Teresa Moon to speak to your school or group or for more information, contact info@instituteforculturalcommunicators.org.